SCAVENGERS

Issue 1.1

Edited & Curated by Shilo Niziolek

Querencia Press, LLC
Chicago, Illinois

SCAVENGERS AN IMPRINT OF QUERENCIA PRESS

ISBN 978 1 959118 49 7

.

www.querenciapress.com

First Published in 2023

Querencia Press, LLC
Chicago IL

Printed & Bound in the United States of America

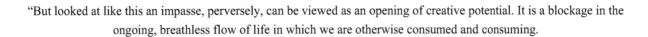

"But looked at like this an impasse, perversely, can be viewed as an opening of creative potential. It is a blockage in the ongoing, breathless flow of life in which we are otherwise consumed and consuming.

In the impasse we encounter the duration of the present. We track what it is like to move throughout the day."

—David Carlin, "Lyrebirds in the Impasse"

CONTENTS

Supercell
—Delilah Martinez

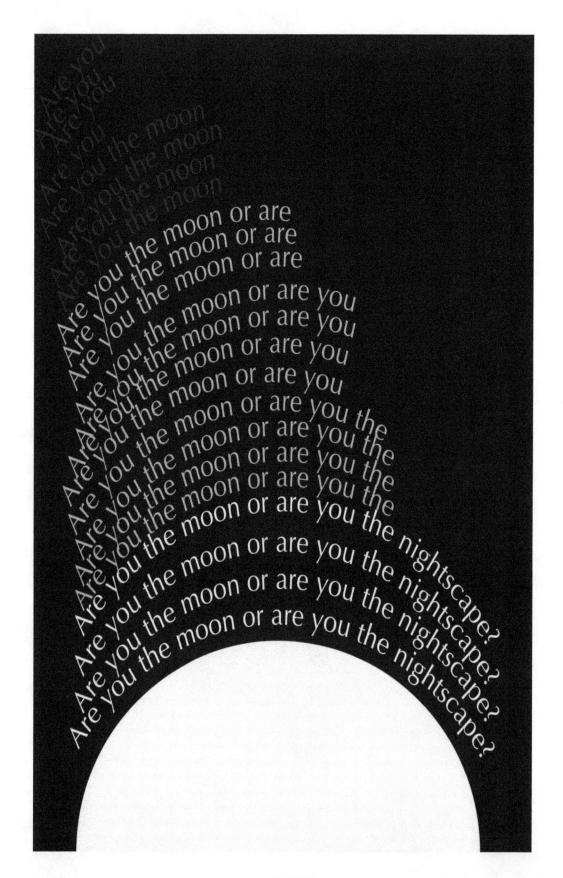

Hurricanes, like thunderstorms need an upwind draft to move and gain intensity. The more organized and visible the eye of the storm, the more destructive. Hurricanes are made when the surface water in the ocean becomes too warm and there is a large temperature gradient between the surface layer and the water below.

A hurricane is a hand mixer let loose.

One of my neighbor's in high school liked to invite me over to make-out. She had a dark brown bob, and sometimes her dad would pick her up from school on his motorcycle. We drank a knock off version of passion-fruit Sunny D and then she'd twirl her hands through my hair. During school she'd trace her hands over my shoulders before class. I didn't like kissing her. Not because she wasn't good at it, but I never felt excited to do it. She'd bite my bottom lip and say, "You're gorgeous". "You're stunning." I'd reply. I didn't want her to love me or leave her boyfriend. I went over to her house to feel desired. Six years later, when I walk past her house, I turn into the direction of her room and wink.

Storm (v.)

"of the wind, "to rage, be violent," c. 1400"

In 2021, Korean indie artist, eAeon came out with his second album titled *Fragile*. The album has a orange traffic cone background with black fading edges. In the center is a series of gray industrial looking shapes in different stages of formation. Some lighter, and other more solid. In a review by Sabrina from *koreaninndie.com* she describes, "the central theme of the album, the fragility of the human soul and its biggest weakness: love."

—Delilah Martinez—

Dear reader,

I have failed to find the map of the soul. Again. Carl Jung suggested that the key to finding ones true self or the soul, was to understand that a person must come to a self-realization. But I have been reflecting too much. So much so, that I feel like a web page that is being constantly refreshed and is now stuck in-between the blankness of reloading and uploading. Jung said that a person must strive to create a balance with the conscious and unconscious in order to obtain a balanced personality and live life to its full potential. So many words to say, I am deflated but will try again tomorrow.

—Delilah Martinez—

CERTIFICATE OF IRREVOCABILITY
—*Darla Mottram*

I.

               Dear

female child   *mom*

do hereby certify   *I miss you*

did duly execute,   *varry*

acknowledge, and deliver   *much evvy*

an instrument in writing   *day and night*

wherein and whereby I   *either criy*

absolutely,   *or thik about*

permanently, and irrevocably   *you*

released, surrendered and relinquished   *I whish*

custody, guardianship,   *nun of this*

and control

all my natural, legal, and parental rights

and privileges of whatever   *hapind betwing us*

with respect to the child, including all my rights   *I awes miss*

in respect to   *you*

the child

II.

        release, surrender, and relinquish

liberat(ion) forfeit(ure) abandon(ment)

                  unfetter(ing) sacrific(ial) forsake(n)

       untie(d) los(t) reject(ion)

                loosen(ing) misplace(d) eliminat(ion)

         untangle(d) forget(ting)   remov(al)

       unravel(ing) neglect(ful) delet(ion)

                        fail(ure) avoid(ance)

             expunge(d)

                  miscarr(iage)

          eras(ure)

                 elu(sive)

—*Darla Mottram*—

III.

what you feel/felt the first time   you hold/held me. little   accident. I am/was not your first
child. nor the first you give/gave away.   if you wish/wished me back

into the womb, if your signature is/was the sound   of someone else's voice,

      the court's voice, *irrevocable.*   do/have I ever live(d)

outside your first wish for me. sometimes I feel I am/was half-   ghost, flitting
between trees a short distance from the village   asking to be let in

      loved, or else   liberated

from this half-   life, this always asking, this hardly knowing
where to put my shaking

      hands.

—Darla Mottram—

A PICTURE GOES IN SEARCH OF A FRAME
—Darla Mottram

I thought I saw you tearing at your eyeballs in morning light—the window did not frame you—were not wearing a Mickey Mouse sweater—your hair was not divided into two crimped pom-poms like that time we went to Disneyland—there was not a wolf stretched between you & the doorway in which I stank / there was not a wolf waiting to swallow you whole—when the window did not break, I did not hear you screaming—stomp it stomp it / let her eat cake—noodles there are noodles in the kitchen a cake half-eaten—cockroaches in the sink—stomp it—there are cock—where are my fucking socks. to look for what you're looking for is to cover your seeing with scales until the only thing seeable is what you've placed in front of you. there was no wolf there was no wolf there was no—at night I enter the wound willingly, it enters me—when I hear the women from good homes say of themselves *imposter syndrome* I wonder if they have ever / been a cockroach / eaten stale cake with bloody fingers—nails bitten to the—cake & ramen for days while Mother disappears into a wolf's mouth. I am ~~looking~~ not looking at myself the imposter & thinking run run ~~away from~~ into the dark.

PRAXIS

—*Darla Mottram*

let's call it *re-traumatization* / in the moonlight the metal gleams / ~~what do you mean he can't remember~~ several times a day I wash my feet, no matter, the grime's too / deep—it surfaces like sidewinder in sand, gold eyes invisible until the instant of / contact—once I was fifteen, then eight, & even for a little while twenty-two, & then a man—& then a man—& then a / *dear statistic,* I fear not the unleashing of the flood but the fluent way we speak of it—all day the lily leaned in / to the mirror & never / did she make passage through glass—look: ~~I've got a problem about men~~ / fifteen times I counted the change on the counter. *how tall are you,* he asks—I think he means, *who gave you the right.* all day rings & several kinds of vanishings— every murder starts the same: someone wants something / the other doesn't want to give—for Mother, it was the ~~remote~~ control.

PRECIOUS
—Darla Mottram

Definitions belong to the definers, not the defined.
—Toni Morrison

in the picture you hold me as if I were—*precious*—
that word I've been told my writing is too—
what does it mean, anyway—to be—*precious*—
wasn't I only saying—you held me like I mattered—
like it would matter if I were removed—
from your *custody*—oh there's another loaded—
& even *loaded*—branches me
I remember—too clearly the school year
beginning my pink coat matching
hat leaves swirling in windy / I almost said / *abandon*—
I remember my friends in school had skin
that was darker than mine, in varying shades & hues,
I remember languages other than English
being spoken I remember later being told—
this is because you were poor—
I remember sitting on the bus waiting
to pick pumpkins, her thin brown arm
intertwined with my thin white arm,
both of us quiet, muffled by whatever it was
we had in common—
the branch snaps / my memory
insists on gaps, blurred spaces—
where might have been—*dear father*—
why did you—it hurts to ask this—
leave me with that man you must have known—
some part of you—were you that desperate—
were you that / *loaded* / I remember
mother waking me before sunrise, driving down
dark roads to see you—you sat behind glass, in *custody*—
your beard grown / longer / it's hard to stay inside—
a *sentence* / splinters / I want out bang bang let me / after
they'd taken me from you—you visited, twice—
the first time was too—*precious*—
bright wind, rustling red & yellow leaves,
the scratch of your beard, the soft of your flannel,
your arms lifting me up, squeal of—

—Darla Mottram—

there's no way to write about it without—it's too—*I'm* too—
the second time / the way I yelled in the white room
with the white walls the white curtains
the white table & bald lights burning—*is this real*—
the absence of color, I mean, not the memory of me yelling for you
to never come back / & you cried / & you didn't—
return—honoring my wish I suppose—
as far back as I remember, I wanted to be alone—
—*is this* real—not the feeling but the story
I tell myself about it—they set a court date—
& when you didn't come (*why didn't you come*)
they severed your / right to parent / is it too *precious*
to say—I didn't expect to never see you again—am I *poor*
for thinking this matters

—*Darla Mottram*—

Mothering

—Hillary Leftwich

—Hillary Leftwich—

Murals

—*Catherine Kyle*

In the city so hot, the tops of your feet burn in minutes—the city where you slide into beanstalks of shade cast by telephone poles while waiting for crosswalk lights to change—you guide a group of children through a weeklong summer camp. This is an art camp, and the students look to you with bright anticipation if they are young, reserved hope if they are older. They want to see what you will do.

Always, you show them watercolors, the way the paint changes if you apply it to dry paper versus wet. You show them how applying wet paint to wet paper causes it to bleed and run into rivulets you couldn't have made on your own. The way the paint develops its own wildness. They practice this, making foxes with galaxies for eyes and sandcastles that reach toward the sky like hands.

Always, taking care that each plastic thermos is filled with cool water and each neon backpack is secure, you wind them through the blazing city until you reach the outdoor gallery of transient murals. They span for blocks, mermaids and butterflies rising up alongside dumpsters and fire hydrants, existing together in a tenuous ecosystem.

The paintings change annually, except for a few permanent ones made from shattered mirrors. The artists who come and refresh the walls create all manner of things—sometimes haunting, sometimes peaceful. A monstrous green face with long, jagged teeth leers out from one shadowed corner. A pig soaring upward with the aid of a balloon decorates the side of a café.

You do not know it yet, but soon, you will shelter inside your home for months, and all the summer camps will be canceled. You do not know it yet, but soon, someone will tell you that you add nothing to the world, that you only take, and you will flee this city like a startled tumbleweed, supernova arrhythmia hammering your chest. You will question the words' truth for months.

For now, though, you are here, hand shielding your eyes from the sun as you smile at the campers. You wander the alleys as the kids take gulps from their bottles, eagerly tap their notebooks with their pencils. *Choose an image,* you tell them, *and write in its voice. Who are you today? Which one speaks to you?* You gaze around at ghosts, roaring serpents, praying angels. *Let them tell you what they have to say.*

Callisto

—*Andrea Lianne Grabowski*

"Crush," Ethel Cain, *Inbred*

Jupiter knew something was off.   Callisto simply said, *you know wha.* not sure if she could even say more. Jupiter listened so well. It couldn't be spoiled. She didn't deserve to hear this all the time.

Callisto had asked her for   had crash-landed instead.

not toe the line, however much she ached

But Jupiter latched her arms around her and   Callisto's chest grew hot.

she would never earn this back. What had she done to be worth it?

reaching up to cup her face, telling her, *take care of yourself, okay?*

Her stitches broke and   resealed.

—*Andrea Lianne Grabowski*—

LEAVING OUT
—Annaliese Jakimides

June Valentine left out of Hudson long before that Tuesday when Harry Valentine dug out another box of ochred photos under the bed. He didn't know why people said photos yellowed; they ochred. Harry hated imprecision.

To be precise, June was 79 when she packed one brand new suitcase small enough for her to carry (she broke a hip two years ago) and big enough to hold two of everything she considered necessary (her list was short), and bright enough (red) for her not to lose it wherever she went (first, the Windswept Motel three blocks away; then the Greyhound bus stop, and finally, an elderhostel in Dallas).

Harry, however, only knew that this time when he told her to get the fuck out if she didn't like it, she did.

Harry untaped the box, and pried open the cardboard flaps. Every week since June left, Harry focused on one year, starting with the first he could remember—1923, when he was five. Forty-one weeks later, his first June memory surfaced, and that's how he found himself in Box #5, 1964–1973.

Green, not ochre, was the color that lay all over the floor in front of his overstuffed chair. A jumble of 20- and 50- and 100-dollar bills and yards of sequined cloth the color of the edge of the ocean on a bilious day settled on the World War II combat boots Harry had taken to pulling on and lacing up before his feet hit the floor to pad to the bathroom each earlier and earlier morning to handle his cock, the one that had always belied his 13EEE boots.

Damn, Harry whispered. No *fuck*. No *shit*. He'd toned his language down in these last months. June hadn't cleaned out their bank account really; she'd cleaned it out sort of. He had $755 when he checked the morning after her leaving— enough for one month's electric, the telephone, the insurance on the trailer, food (both cat and people), plus money to fix the incessant drip-drip-drip of a leak in the roof he had refused to hire someone to do, insisting he would do it himself for the 533rd time.

Harry kicked his camouflaged feet through the sparkles back and forth, watching the crumpled-up bills flip over his boot tops, until he spied the corner of a tree and one of his big ears. He lifted the photo up, into the morning sun, and watched him and June under an umbrella tree in the Congo pavilion at the New York World's Fair. June was smiling and laughing. He heard her mouthing *Bouma, Kasai, Luba*. Oh, how she loved the foreign names.

Harry then knew every single dollar would be in Box #5, and #6 and #7 and #8. She'd bought the photos: bought back all the memories, except this one of her and him at the beginning, in the light, when naming was a possibility.

—Annaliese Jakimides—

You're Gonna Need a Bigger Room

> *after Molly Peacock and The White Stripes*
> —*Jill Michelle*

All the doctors who can't help before 27 weeks t**L**
me to move as little as possible, say gravity and **I**
must only be bedfellows, he already having emp**T**
d my womb 6 weeks too soon in a duplicate, cat**T**
corner room, turning each door swing to bombsh**L**
each delivered meal into memory shrapnel that br**E**

ches the present, 11 months later, with its same d**R**
k mirror of TV screen, same water cup. First sorr**O**
not even toddling age, crawls the tiled floors, foll**O**
ing the bright-scrubbed nurses, screaming over th**M**.

On Voting

after Wisława Szymborska's "Lesson"
—*Jill Michelle*

Subject Donald Trump *predicate* tries to steal a *direct*
object election with his *indirect objects* words, herds,
pleas, felonies, whatever-means-necessary mentality.
Subject senators *predicate* vote on *indirect object* impeachment

adverb again[1]. *Adjectives* Another white *subject* man *predicates*
feels entitled, attempts to take *direct objects* liberties, property,
ownership, advantage of the *indirect objects* weaker, darker, poorer
man, woman, person, camera, TV, situation *adverbs*
historically, illegally, relentlessly, again.

Adjectives Another white man's news *subject* story *predicate*
parsing *direct objects* words, rules, procedures, *predicate*
knowing *direct object* right from *indirect object* wrong *predicate*
reframing the *direct objects* narrative, history, laws *predicate*
to suit his own *direct object* ends *adverb* again.

[1]https://www.nytimes.com/interactive/2021/02/13/us/politics/senate-impeachment-live-vote.html

—*Jill Michelle*—

Love or Lose
   —*Christina D. Rodriguez*

—*Christina D. Rodriguez*—

another video
—Reverie Koniecki

Have you seen the video yet? my husband asks. I am not going to watch another black man die on film, I say. I dodge the bullet of reality with a list of shoulds and should nots. black death should be dignified. black death shouldn't be a spectacle. black death shouldn't be trusted to the talons of the police. black death shouldn't be a preemptive sentence. Lies I tell myself: if I don't watch, I'll stop the loop of him dying over and over again. if I don't watch, I'll be able to breathe without the american dream tightening around my throat, if I look away, it won't hurt so much. think of the mothers with their cavernous sorrow and open wombs cocooning their bodies as they watch their boys get pulled from existence. boys who could've been mine with confident smiles and youthful swagger. the boy is mine. the imprint of his first howls in the world. a clenched fist for a nipple and hungry grunts. a body curled like a kidney bean. the squeak of his swing as it propels back and forth in simulated flight. the mutual longing for his head on my chest. firsts. birthday. riding a bike. girlfriend. heartache. dying. think of the mothers as their flesh is separated from the bone as their sons' bodies are left for carrion eyes.

When your oldest daughter gets mono,

—Reverie Koniecki

you make apple ginger tea in the crockpot. You ruminate about the health properties of cinnamon and fresh ginger. How they're supposed to be the cure all for everything. How the vitamin c from the freshly cut apples and limes will surely boost her immune system. You stir and think about how last night was the first time in years she'd asked you for a massage. And how surprised you were to discover that she still has that dry patch of raised skin on her left ankle. And how automatically your fingers traveled back in time to when you first brought her home from the hospital to that tiny two bedroom apartment in N. Ames Street. You are surprised that you still remember the detail of the pink-flower-swirling-green-stem-wallpaper. The green cushioned rocker and its matching moving ottoman that you'd put together yourself. You are surprised at how much your body aches for the absence of hers, how time has cleaved your bodies further and further apart.

This is the peninsula that broke off and became an island;

you think of the first time your mother drove you over the Chesapeake Bay Bridge as you knead her elongated legs. You wonder if she'll have more mercy than you, who just stood there in the lobby of Davidson Hall for a nanosecond before offering your mother a pageant wave and rising to the fourth floor where you would bloom into a freshman. You wonder if she'll allow you to cradle her one last time, If she'll pretend to not be embarrassed at your sentimentality. You roll your thumbs over the birthmark on her back. You remember how you used to give her lavender baths in the sink. You want to lift her. To accordion those arms and legs so she fits into your lap again. You want to hold her head fast to your chest as if both of your lives depend on this contact. You want to rock her till she falls asleep. To listen to each breath. You want to believe that each collapse of her chest will be followed by a subsequent rise.

Speak All Evil
—Andi Benet

—Andi Benet—

seven things i bought because of you

> *after "anything" by Adrianne Lenker and "Dragon New Warm Mountain I Believe In You" by Big Thief*
> —*Andrea Lianne Grabowski*

california citrus kombucha, $3.99, tom's market

photographed in my car. couldn't tell you soon enough. nectar from your home poured into a crystal glass. drained on my nightstand, movie over, opening my chest with the press of a call button. the sun drenched the citrus for harvest & fermentation. they say icarus flew too close to it. "what a reckless boy." but who can blame him for the warmth in his chest when he looked at that golden star? of course he tried to fly. maybe his life on land hurt too much. the flight must've been beautiful. but he only had wax to hold him up. if i could rewrite that story, i'd say that the beauty of the sun & the knowledge of the wax & the desire to leave the pain of the land behind wove him a tapestry to lift him out of the water, wove him wings to fly.

one hundred nights of hero by isabel greenberg, $3.99, pangobooks

i got it used. happened to be an ex-library copy. the sticker on the back cover: san francisco public library. serendipity. like the meteor. i read it aloud to my grandmother, read it in the car, absorbing the fairy tales told in drawn panels, in all their rawness, tenderness, ache. story of two girls turned into stars in heaven, almost as bright as the smallest moon. the legends called them the twins, the eyes, the lovers, the heroes.

monterey strawberry chobani yogurt, $1.25, oryana community co-op

serendipity. like how you used to have the same phone case as me. how i got your favorite kombucha—pineapple peach— without knowing. how halsey's "colors" played in the los angeles airport. how taylor's "lover" played as we walked into the pharmacy. how we notice these little things & let them be beautiful.

it's a 10 miracle leave-in product, $12.99, meijer

borrowing a smidge from your bottle. my hands smoothing it through my wet hair. dancing with the dust below the ceiling fan. your hair gleaming with copper strands in the sun, gathered at the nape of your neck with a simple black scrunchie. drenched by lakewater, your hands slicking it back from your face, nearly black against your shoulders. i carry you bridal style over a wave cresting at my chest. our lips trading water droplets from the saltless ocean that has been my lifelong regulator, playmate. we were shining *in the barrel of the hot sun*, silvie *has a little if we need some, q. has a ride if we want to come, shoulder of* my *shirt sleeve slipping.* a week later i stand in the supermarket aisle & wait for the photo of the hair product to deliver. the bottle is dark purple, magenta cap. didn't use it for a month. used it yesterday.

cera ve hydrating face wash, $3.69, target

actually, this was because of my doctor. i have called myself an excellent mimic. laying on someone else's couch the color of pistachios, my tears coughing up flames—*copycat, i don't want to be one anymore.* you, a silver-tongued dragon in my phone line, as i sat in my car watching the moon rise over scruffy sand dune pines: *do what you like, wear what you like.* i like the face wash. i turn the label around. i turn it back to face me. the label is your favorite color. this is not the one you use.

—*Andrea Lianne Grabowski*—

bottle of tajín seasoning, $2.69, aldi

unopened, for now. california thunderstorms are so short. michigan ones so long we must pull the sheets off the clothesline, watch the lighting over the circle of pines and red oaks, quiet enough i can hear you blink. spinning fantasies, for now, but family? the limits of that love are different. like the sea. *dragon in the new warm mountain, didn't you believe in me?* when i finally open the tajín, i will give you a picture of my grandmother & i eating it sprinkled on slices of mango.

a mango, 89 cents, aldi

sliced on my mother's wooden cutting board, like the one we shared on the blanket at the dusky shore of platte lake the first day we saw each other. adrianne has a song about mangoes, juice dripping. clotheslines, soothing hands. i kissed your eyes because of that song. & i hear she wrote it about a lover who is no longer a lover. there's salt in the sea you can sometimes see from your window. there's no salt in lake michigan. mangoes could only grow indoors here. maybe they could thrive in the town you grew up in. you held my silence, said words i couldn't—scared, but wanting to. & i don't know if adrianne talks to indigo anymore, but she says she & buck are *deep friends.* oh, how songs & fruit help make sense of things. so much i'd never known. so much we still don't. so much we still can. *i don't wanna talk about anything.* but we wanted to talk about everything. we still do. adrianne's new album, with buck, with other friends, is called *dragon new warm mountain i believe in you.* & the closing refrain of the title track—*it's a little bit magic.*

—Andrea Lianne Grabowski—

Page 2
—Donica Larade

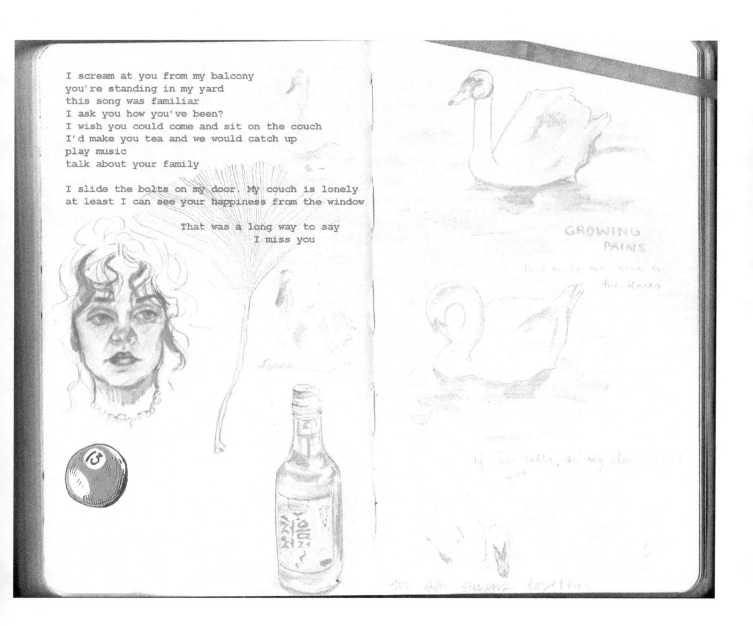

Picture Theory

—Tim Horvath

From the way the corks have piled up in here, one might think drinking problem. They call it a drinking problem as if the problem is doing the drinking. If you could name it for the real cause maybe you could end the problem. What we have is thus a language problem. Said not Wittgenstein, but it was the kind of thing he would've said. The kind of thing he would say now. If we could design an AI, WittgenstAIn, that would just spit out Wittgensteinian observations continuously. Wittgenschtick. It'd be so effective you'd throw on power-saving mode just to get some relief from its brilliance.

Wittgenstein would've had some fun with "cork," the idea of "uncorking." To uncork is to shift a cork from a place of higher pressure to one of lower pressure. You can only uncork certain things. You can't uncork, say, a walrus. I mean, maybe you could, if you moved a walrus from a place of higher pressure to one of lower pressure. But getting a walrus to move is labor-intensive, and the things that cause walruses to feel under pressure are quite different from what corks face. Are multifaceted and complex and have to do with larger patterns in the ecosystem, disruptions of habitat, in the food chain. Also loud noises. Still, if you tried to uncork a walrus, it probably would not happen without some pushback. A cork, stubborn enough. The chances Wittgenstein ever saw a live walrus are slim. The chances Wittgenstein ever uncorked a walrus still slimmer. Wittgenstein himself, slim if we go by pictures. Most walruses are not slim, though alas likely getting slimmer, and not by choice. The chances that Wittgenstein dreamed of a walrus at some point are greater than the chances that he laid eyes on one. Eyes not odds. I have never seen a picture of a chance, even swimming away.

Home

—Carella Keil

—Carella Keil—

Italicized Shame Heard Round The World

—Jillian Calahan

It's *that time of the month* again. That time when *the thing comes.* The *little clown with a nosebleed.* My *eldest aunt, Emma,* has arrived at my doorstep. With her *apple bread, tomato juice,* and *red balloon.* She sits at my kitchen table, drinking her *red tea* like an *old friend.* But she's not, she is a *monster.* A *vampire* dressed as *little red riding hood.* Don't let her fool you, she's *bad luck* and she knows your *devils.* I hear her *grumbling.* "*The cranberry woman is coming.*" But I ignore her and pour myself another *bloody mary.* I have *lady business* to take care of and don't have time for her nonsensical *code red* warnings. I need to get dinner started. I *cook black pudding* while *defrosting the steak,* leaving a *big red* puddle of *mad cow disease* and *bloody murder* on the counter. But, *the carrots are cooked,* so that's one less thing I need to worry about. And the news says *there are communists in the funhouse.* If things get as bad as they say, we will need to leave and *check into the red roof inn.* What a *blue day* that will be. For I simply cannot go. *I have a flood* because *it's raining on the farm* and I'm *having the painters in* to cover the *red wave* that coats the walls of my halls. It's all so overwhelming. Now the steaks have burned and my *Aunt* has left for the *blood festival.* I am alone. I scream a *crimson wave* through the air, *birthing blood diamonds* from my eyes. My body, a temple of pain. From my *redhead* to my toes. The house feels like it's crumbling around me. I run outside, bottle in one hand, lighter in the other. I hold fire to *the rag* I've soaked in gasoline, tossing it through the window. I watch it burn and walk away.

Now *Granny's stuck in traffic* at the *red traffic light* that never changes. Which is to say, granny is dead. It brings me peace. And as the *red moon* rises, I think of how ridiculous this story is. And how much easier it would have been to just say "I'm on my *period.*"

Midull

—Donica Larade

At the Intersection of Hope and 7th Street

—Alexis Dinkins

You lifted your face up toward the street light and the cords of your neck tensed and pulled. I wondered what music you'd make if I played those strings, settled a kiss along them. I watched you breathe, nostrils flared, your chest silently expanding, and I wanted to be as close to you as the eyelash dancing on the hill of your cheekbone. I settled for picking it up with the pad of my finger, and watching your lips O as you wished it away with a puff of air.

I followed you up to your apartment, climbed all those stairs, drank a vodka lemonade on your couch. We danced, you came to me soft and unraveled me, like yarn released from its core. When we finally woke up next to each other and neither our waking nor our coupling was new, the memory stayed sweet and easy until it was time to go home again, and welcome the whistle of the switch through the air and the backhand across the mouth.

The next time I saw you I wore magnesium to keep from smelling myself, a yellow ribbon for the gold I would not inherit. Bloodshed eyeliner so the ancestors saw what they left behind, bangles so they could hear me coming. The necklace I bought from the woman who spoke in tongues on the corner for armor. And so that the ancestors would hear my pleas whenever I called for him, the baby I would name Femi. He was still small within me, and I had to go to work.

To keep from losing him, I sat eyes closed, full sun, no SPF, pussy pressed soft to stone. Let my breasts hang down to my knees, let a hurricane swallow my screams. I knit little baby socks to go on his little baby feet. Chained dandelions into a cradle, wove them, wilted and unwilling, into something to hold him to me. Cut my nails to nubs and bit them to the bone. Drank only chamomile and honeysuckle.

Bled and bled and bled

Braided my hair back and left it to frizz. Let them fondle. Let them scrape me clean: a watermelon rind.

—Alexis Dinkins—

Long After I'm Gone, My Hair

—Francesca Leader

will be
in drains
in carpets
in asphalt
in birds' nests.
in the lining of that coat of mine you like (the one with the hole in the pocket).
in landfills
in sewer pipes
in raindrops
in the ocean's   black deep, and (if I may wish it)
in between your back teeth, lover, that you might savor the memory of how it came
to lodge there, and be all right,
long after,
long after
I'm   gone.

—Francesca Leader—

the novel believes in you

—Yael Villafranca

—Yael Villafranca—

ON RELATING TO MY SURROUNDINGS

—Celeste Perez

I fear the *yesterday* and the *now* of it. The way it sounds out   past tense   as I square my mouth

in the   face of   *tomorrow.* The lemon on the table   dried when I sliced myself a wheel.

Was killed when plucked from branch.   Died still   when first buried   only to meet my hands

weeping salt   over each pearl gleaming yellow   growing smaller   as it turns in the air.

It is like a child   darling and tall   glowing darling and taller   away from you:

On my niece's first day I oblige to mourning   and gratefully.   Fetch me my black band!

Let midnight sprout Eternal on my left side.   Watch as I spoon the day's ashes into my pillow

for just this morning   I could fit Her inside the iris of my heart.   *Oh strange and constant spring!

Do not ask me   of the humanity. This is it.   Go back to sanctuary   for the eyes have it.

I will remain   long as I am   growing small   but far   body half-mast

sighing ashes into my pillow   *goodnight, goodnight*   the dawn is hardly a whisper.

*This line is borrowed from Lia Purpura's essay, "Of Prayer"

—Celeste Perez—

ELEGY OF MY VERY OWN

—Celeste Perez

A late sun   swells the eye socket
     I call it
The Grand Thickening

Among the damp lung
     mornings pregnant with lilac
and gum disease
     I reach for chins paternal and firm
to find   the Darling Ghost of my trembling
face   hidden among Her   quiet labors

     In the mirror She is holding
I see   people   pass
graciously through my life
     and in the way I prefer to remember

How far we are from first breath

She sings   to the tusk of each star
     above us
     and shaking
     a warm coronet
     a clasp for my tender head

How can I compete with The Hours?

I breathe   then wake   to humming
     the coffee stains
     the burnt sugar of dusk

and   the   wind

     the wind

how it ushers
     the circular haunt of living

SO LONG, SMALL FIGMENT (A fragment)

—Celeste Perez

It isn't

easy

/ /

I am not

so good

//

dear friend

dear friend

//

sympathy heart

not to be

//

how wonderful

confused and human

//

you have your own way

I see

//

your face:

      it *is—*

Please Sign My Petition About the Wolves

—Katy Haas

The wolves gather during golden hour. They've spent all day sharpening their teeth and when they laugh like coyotes, their canines reflect the sun into each other eyes.

The wolves take turns lifting their paws into the air and contorting them until the shadows do their bidding. They form human heads and puppeteer conversations about stocks and celebrities. They think about how fun it would be if they were the heroes in the stories about little girls and grandmas, if they were on Wall Street, if they were Leo DiCaprio. They'd survive the Titanic. They'd beam into dreams and convince everyone they were the good guys all along, their fur lit up by sunset, a halo, something wholesome and holy that would never swallow anyone whole.

The wolves take photos of other wolves for their social media accounts that they caption with #goldenhourgoodguys and #nofilternofangs. They like each other's photos and then leave positive reviews for the new vegan restaurant downtown. They rave about the sweet potato steak on a bed of quinoa with roasted pine nuts and the most delicious sauce drizzled on the side, and don't get them started on the crème brûlée that they never would have guessed was plant-based.

When the sun sinks behind the horizon, the wolves kiss each other's cheeks and head home, avoiding the shadows that once hid their slinking frames. They water their gardens that grow dahlias and daisies. They eat warm dinners and brush their sharp teeth and then tuck their kids into bed. They read them stories and in the stories they build houses for pigs and escort lost girls through forests and bake pies with nice grannies who give them makeovers with their own granny clothes. When young boys cry wolf, the whole town cheers and welcomes the wolf into their homes. In these stories, the wolves do good whenever they can.

The wolves retire to the family room to watch the evening news and turn it off early when the newscaster warns viewers a pack of wolves was seen gathering at sunset. The newscaster says their objective was unknown but be careful: lock your doors and windows, walk your kids to and from school, call grandma and make sure she's not a monster in disguise. They go to bed and stare up at the dark ceiling, their eyes pale moons glowing as they think of what it means to be a monster. As they think about how, despite what the stories say, the big bad wolf will never die.

Dancers

—*Francesca Leader*

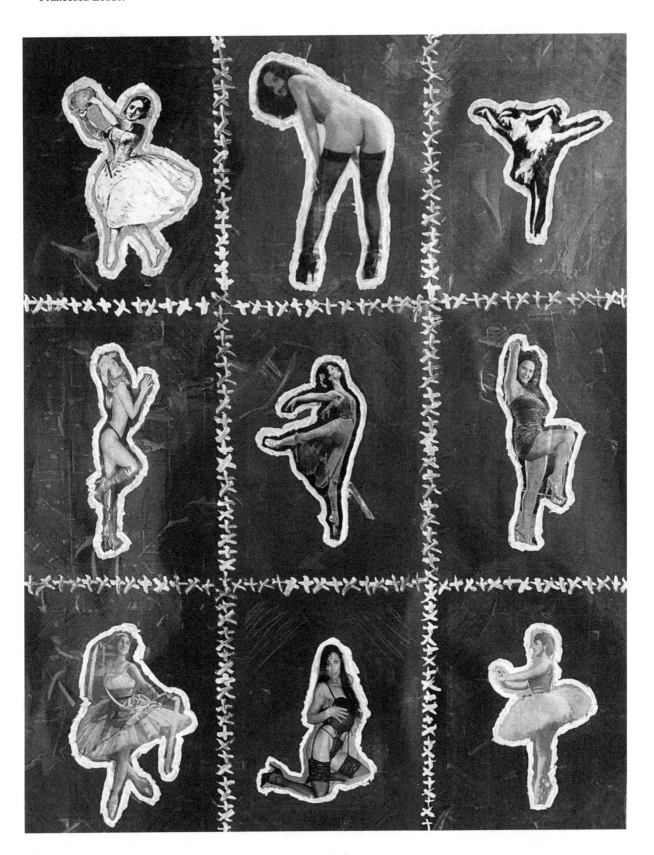

—*Francesca Leader*—

SWEETNESS

—Annaliese Jakimides

Mama spooned thick black raspberry ice cream from the carton. The women hummed over her thin-lined shoulders like black hornets over summer sweetness. I hung at her feet under the table.

Daddy's face sat in a direct line from me, our eyes eating up each other quiet-like and inconceivable slow. The beanbag chair scooped Daddy's body, his arms spread open wide like Pastor Adams preaching about hell and all those titty shows the men got caught watching in the church basement last week.

Mama slurped another spoonful, and another, little raspberry lines trickling down her chin.

"Hildy, ain't that been enough?" asked her best friend. Mama's teeth smiled into the carton, then up at the buzzing women flapping hankies in the hard air over Mama and her spoon and her hungers. "I'm gonna have it all," Mama said. Her tongue licked the box out; her fingers crushed the cardboard; her feet slipped into the slick black patent leather pumps by the table leg just a heartbeat from my knees; and out the busted front door went Mama, strutting and shuffling and twirling a little in her dancing shoes.

The sirens wailed like the mad street dogs Daddy always said they was.

Suddenly, all of a piece, the women moved from the table to the chair, their flighty hands pumping the air, multicolored wings of impossible angels. A raspberry color spotted Daddy's still lips.

Who woulda thought Mama needed to go dancing that bad?

—Annaliese Jakimides—

Guts

—Aidan Jung

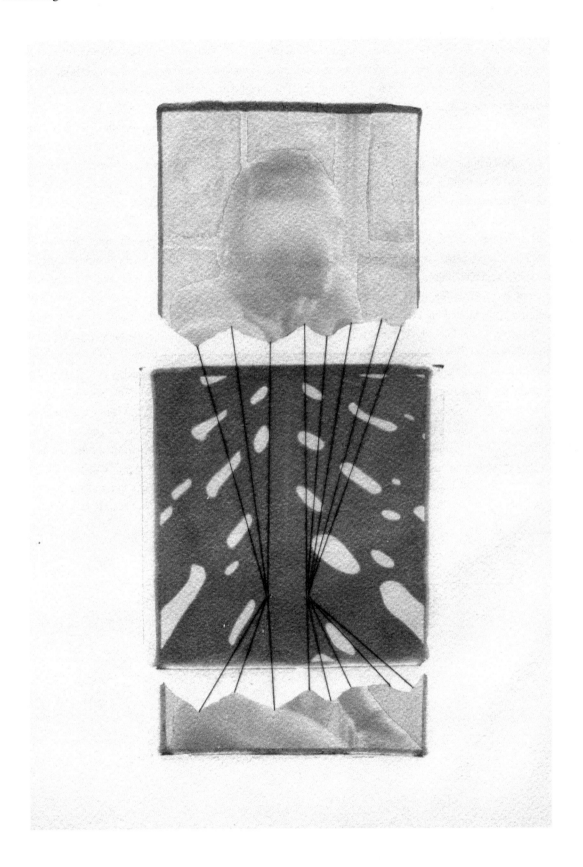

—Aidan Jung—

It's All on Ice, Alright

—C.E. O'Banion

Hey, Melissa, good morning, um, you may or may not listen to this message, but I was just saying hi, and did you ever think of a gift card idea for Casey– this is going to be kind of a gift card Christmas for the grown-ups, like, I have some ideas for others, like for example James, I gave him a gift card to Specs because he likes to drink, and David, I think I'm giving him a big gift card because he won't buy anything big for himself, you know, so maybe to some hipster cool store that I've never even heard about, and Mary Claire suggested this cool golf store place for Brent's – it's like an online golf store I think, so perfect for a gift card anyway. I just can't think of really anything for Casey. If you had an idea that would be great, helpful, whatever if you don't – I'll just come up with something. O-kay. I hope you're having a good day. I'm kind of having a whiplash day coming home from the lake and Katie's, and I'm trying to get my things in order because Katie is bringing her kids tomorrow, so I'm kind of losing the weekend anyway. All good. It's all good. Big tree on the house from the storm, but, you know, other than that everything is pretty great here. O-Kay, I will just, just… think maybe nothing too exotic but somewhere Casey would like to spend a gift card – it's not that personal of a gift, I guess, but you get the point – just something fun and unique to the person. I don't need another scene. What's something he would enjoy using but it's basic enough to even have a gift card because, you know, a lot of places don't even have gift cards like that little coffee shop he likes, I'm sure they're too cool for a gift card, but would he drink Starbucks if I gave it to him? I doubt he cares much. I didn't even know he drank coffee, to be honest. Oh, well. I'm looking out the kitchen window at this pine on the garage. It's huge – *hugh-mun-gous*. Missed the Ferrari though or else Dennis would have just died. What else do you want for Christmas? Anything to eat? I could do Charlotte Russe but probably not time for that! Making the gumbo here. Hope the TSA is in a good mood when we go through security. They thought I was crazy bringing frozen trout in our carry-ons last time – Dennis said we should check them, but I thought that might be suspicious. Not in a hijack-y sort of way, but just in a who brings frozen trout on an airplane sort of way. Really. If you didn't know Dennis, you'd think he was still an 18-wheeler driver. All he wants are new compression socks for Christmas, so I got him the kind Brett Favre is always modeling on T.V. He's worried the beer he's going to leave out for the garbage men will freeze since it's going to be, you know, below freezing. I told him, *Dennis, you can give them beer another time*, or they can probably get their own beer, but he loves doing that, so he rigged some system out there to keep the beer warm enough so it won't freeze, and they can have it Christmas Day. He calls it "rodeo cold" because that's how they serve them at rodeos, like he's ever been to a rodeo. The dogs are chasing the neighbor, I can see them from the window. Daisy! No! O-Kay, all right, all right, I have to run. Thanks, bye…

—C.E. O'Banion—

bittersweet [recovered]

—nat raum

file_under> "bittersweet [recovered]"

spine to sternum, like serving spoons,
i wonder if you notice when i enter
the room and my eyes refuse to break

contact; i wonder (in hatred) why you
don't bare your teeth like i do at the thought
of belonging to someone else.

—nat raum—

Bifurcated Hairscape

 —Kate Garklavs

—Kate Garklays—

Hand Me Down Haunting

—*Rebecca Lauer*

The pawn shop looked like any other, except for the iron bars and netting installed across both sides of the windows. Keep the vibes in and the people out. There was nothing out of the ordinary about this place nestled on 14th and Belmont. A small parking lot felt huge in the gridlock of mid-day Portland. Old things lined the shelves near the windows, old guitars hung from the walls while the cameras and jewelry lived behind locked cases. Where else could the kids of Portland steal comics and cheap trading cards?

The driver leaned into the backseat and grabbed a cardboard box. Another day another shopper. What treasure would waltz in today? The doorbell, still a bell hung at the top of the frame, rang twice. "Welcome in," she said to the young man approaching her counter.

Edith worked alone during the day. A grey-haired-part-time-employee who enjoyed the job that ate up the hours before the sun went down and she could go home and watch TV. A shiny new corolla pulled into the middle of three spaces outside the shop.

He set the box down. One of those awkward kids who'd never been taught how to do things on their own. "My grandpa had these in his office in his house." He said. "We're… we cleaned the place." He put stress on the fact everything was said and done." He stammered on a few ums before saying, "I also read this place buys *haunted* items."

"We used to be the only place on this side of the river that even touched ouija boards." Edith turned her head and thought back, all those years ago, when the owner's wife slipped and cut her eye open with a broken wine glass, but we don't talk about that… no, it didn't matter… it's a fluke, right? She went sober after that but she kept on buying those boards and boxed herself in the attic upstairs that burned down. Those were the easy ghosts to handle and Edith was pretty good at her job. "What's the haunting?" He didn't answer so she opened the box and found nothing much: a broken hand mirror, mason jars, rusted keys, then dozens of pebbles mixed with animal bones left at the bottom of the box. Edith remembered the doll brought back from a hunting trip that rearranged kitchen knives. "Hearing about the haunting helps with the price."

"I don't care about the money," he said. "Hell, I'd pay you to take it."

This was supposed to be bargaining, not a plea deal. Edith said, "Tell me what's happening."

"Everything was fine," he said, "until I cleaned out these weird jars we found in my grandma's closet. I broke the wax seal of them and the nastiest water you've ever smelled was in there, probably from all the rusty nails and keys with notes on the lid about how much she hated my grandpa. And when I went to pour it out in my yard-"

"You *didn't.*" Don't judge the customers. That never goes well.

—*Rebecca Lauer*—

"Three weeks later I started having nightmares. The worst things you could imagine, dying. Then I'd wake up and see my girlfriend sitting on the edge of the bed looking up at the ceiling, like something was talking to her and she was just listening. But my dogs weren't barking. The internet said I only had to be worried if your pets start barking at the wall. I remembered this store and hoped you were still open." He looked at the box. "*That* is everything my girlfriend says is haunted."

Edith used a cloth to handle the items, taking them out and setting them to the side one by one. "How 'bout these rocks." She shook the box of stones of different colors collected in the same cardboard.

"Pops brought those back from beaches." The kid rolled his eyes. "He was in the Army for *years*…" This was an old story told at holidays, over and over as his grandfather lost his mind. "So he sent a pebble back to my grandma whenever he could. Then, when they got older they went around bickering in their RV to all the national parks and ghost towns picking rocks."

Edith set the box down and whispered. "What?"

"It's all their tourist crap," he said. "I mean stuff. You really won't take it?"

"No," Edith said. "I won't."

"What's so bad about a couple rocks and animal bones?" he asked.

"They stole it," Edith said. "Obviously…." She could replace the frame of that mirror, sell the keys and jars to customers with bad attitudes, but there was nothing she could do about an old man's lifetime of taking from the world. "Is it your money or his you'd pay me with?"

"Please," the kid said. "I really *need* your help. This has to stop."

She pushed the box away from her. "I don't want to get tangled with that," Edith said. "The only thing I can think of to solve the problem is putting everything back where it goes."

"But, but," he stammered. "They're from all over."

"Your grandpa must've loved to travel," Edith said. "It's nice he took your grandma on vacations to hate him during and left you a box of stolen and haunted stuff."

"He's the one who took it," he said. "Why should it matter that he passed it down to me?"

"The first step of any haunting is to accept you have one," Edith said. "After that it's like learning how to walk, one step after another until you're out of my store on the street in a world built for people like him who will be gone soon. Like us one day too." She didn't feel a bit sorry for the diagnosis she gave. Maybe a little rambling. What were the voices trying to tell her now? "Ghosts hate when you steal."

—Rebecca Lauer—

Heart of December

—*Dia & Beppi – Pink Zombie Rose Project*

—Dia & Beppi – Pink Zombie Rose Project—

—Dia & Beppi – Pink Zombie Rose Project—

—*Dia & Beppi – Pink Zombie Rose Project*—

—Dia & Beppi – Pink Zombie Rose Project—

—Dia & Beppi – Pink Zombie Rose Project—

Know the Origin of My Eat

—Kelly Gray

In an effort to murder me,

> my mother wrapped her brittle
> chains around the refrigerator,

let me peer in.   A frozen cake,   resplendent.

Now, when you try to build family with me, I arrive with cutting boards for hands. The lemons I steal from the tree of my childhood are summer-sour, I can never wait for winter, the smell of pine escapes me. When night comes, you teach me to prepare squid by placing your hands over mine. It reminds me of the inside of an infant's arm, the body is too soft. Is a mother good just because she has knees we can grab and sink our faces into, hiding. She is not. I want to explain to you that it was a wedding cake, meant to stack and signify the years. I carved out the back with bent fork, ate her husbandly intentions as if it could feed me: enough. Sweet buttercream broke into pink waves along the edges, there the tsunami begins. Watch my hair sink upwards towards that one bright spot at the top of water and linoleum. I want to look into the face of jellyfish and see you there with undulating arms and sea things that I think are love. You have filled the pantry with life jackets and yet listen to the hand crank radio like I am the inverse feed of gluttony. If I find the sac of ink in the innards, can I float out into the universe and give over to the buzz of electronics? Hum with me. I step into the radio and change the station until I am so far from that sunken kitchen where I first knew my mother was kneeless. She had no bend.

I swim towards channels while refrigerator doors open,

all the cakes floating out and up,   filling the holes of light.
My dead throat,   just a little alive,

gulping.

—Kelly Gray—

The Agaric Dream of the Woodland Reindeer

—Kelly Gray

Boreal, boreal, September.   Caribou
bellow rut.   My mother holds
her antlers
          till she slops me

from womb,   her tongue blood hot
when she licks me.
See me   spindle legs,   lichen eater,
          steam mouth,

milk drinker.   Birch trees
give way to amanitas, amanitas
            to slumber,
I give way

to dream myself
a human,   my hands more knuckle
then ungulate.
      Snow finds the shape

      of my eyelashes a bedframe.
I have a desk   and perfume.
I hinge   at a pelvis.
I stay too long,   writing.

My human mind sets
to learn   migration.
To mark   river crossings

back to self.   I seek   tundra,
parkas   made of hide.
I miss   my mother's stench,
      her hooves expanding

in the wake of green.
I remember   she stood within drifts.
Now,   she calls till I wake
in ice nest   of sedge,

our primordial
     calving grounds.
        I drop my head
           against blizzard, my people
               clicked-kneed
                   and flying.

—Kelly Gray—

birbs (in earthlessness)
   —*Ami J. Sanghvi*

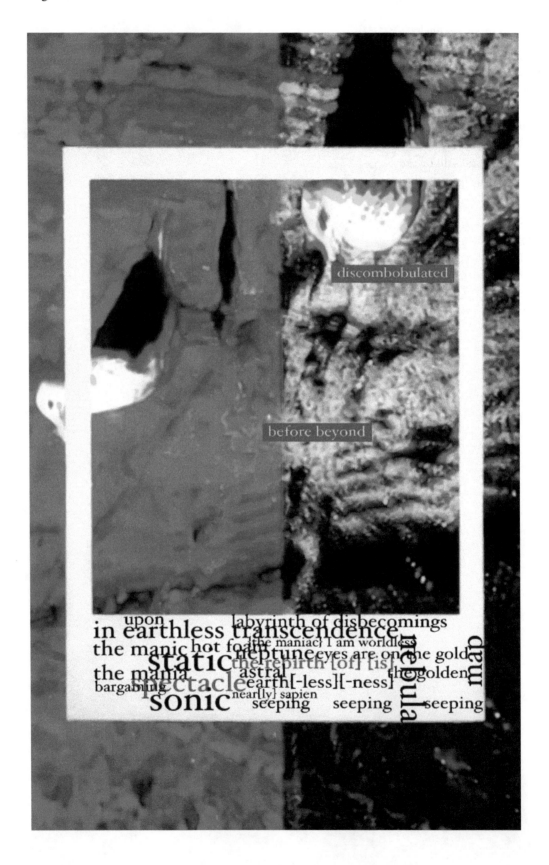

—*Ami J. Sanghvi*—

All Intact

—Crystal Sansom

A chunk of animal fur lay in the backyard, the breeze dusting the concrete pad with the clump. Back and forth it passed, forcing the wind to tumble it, but never leaving the patio. Katie wondered if the animal it belonged to was dead. The pile was the size of her palm, not so much that the animal was surely dead, just enough to make it plausible.

Katie's phone fell out of her lap, the clank of the metal hitting the concrete below. Even the phone jumped away. She checked the screen, lit up, all intact, no notifications. Inside was her mother, a pie forcing her to bake it. Her mother's mania had returned in full force yesterday. The house was clean now. Through the backdoor window, Katie could see her mother's arms were splashed with cherry juice.

She was home from school, her mother at her sister's house. Outside her window, a yelp and screech, throaty yet high-pitched – two cats, fighting in a bundle. Katie had never seen either before. She looked on as they tore chunks from each other, for no reason except they were both there at the same time.

The cats had gone, and Katie took a Mason jar from the kitchen. On the back porch, more tufts of fur left. Katie packaged the soft tumbleweeds in the jar, the balls of fluff the opposite of the violence that harvested them. She pressed the fur between her fingers before sealing up the jar. Drops of blood dotted the concrete. When she ran her finger over the spots, they were already dry under the sun.

Her mother returned, a kitten in her arms. She had gone to the shelter after visiting her sister. She felt Katie needed companionship. The next time her mother left, Katie put the cat in the backyard, hoping tumbleweeds would fall from his coat when the other cats returned.

90%

—*Tiffany Overby*

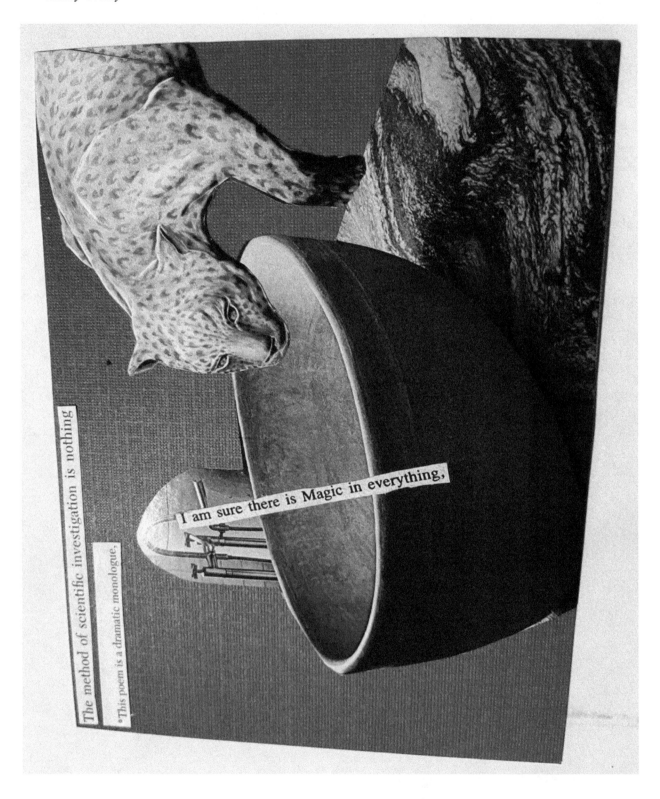

—*Tiffany Overby*—

Although

—Tiffany Overby

I'm the human here

I'm the H. sapiens
    Do you hear me

I'm the Hominidae family
    Even though
    it doesn't matter
    I have to say it aloud anyways

I'm a beast too

—Tiffany Overby—

Passages
  —*Maddie McGalliard*

— *Maddie McGalliard*—

Passages

—Maddie McGalliard

Let me be aimless
And traverse this dicey terrain
With the cloud-covered moon at my back.
Let me survey the darkness
And curse the absence of light
With piercing silent screams.
Let me follow the echoes
And run wildly through the stillness
With bare and blistered feet.
Let me be healed
And free to wander the obscure landscape
With a deep understanding of the night.

headphones

—Donica Larade

On Exhibition

—Kyra Lambert

You're not actually confined to the exhibit in their head

She croaked from the chair beside my bed

Her head leaned back so a sliver of sun sat on her bottom lip

This seemed to punctuate her thought even further

The smoke from the spliff we shared

Curled and twisted around her exhale

I know how she tells which oranges are ready

I know how she smells when she first wakes up

And which stop signs in town she only pauses at

but

To have a spiral interrupted by the perfect dance of words

To quiet those feelings of confinement

She told me

You're not actually confined in the exhibit in their head

The latch is right there

if there's a cure for this / i don't want it—diana ross

—Yael Villafranca

—Yael Villafranca—

WHYFCKR

—nat raum

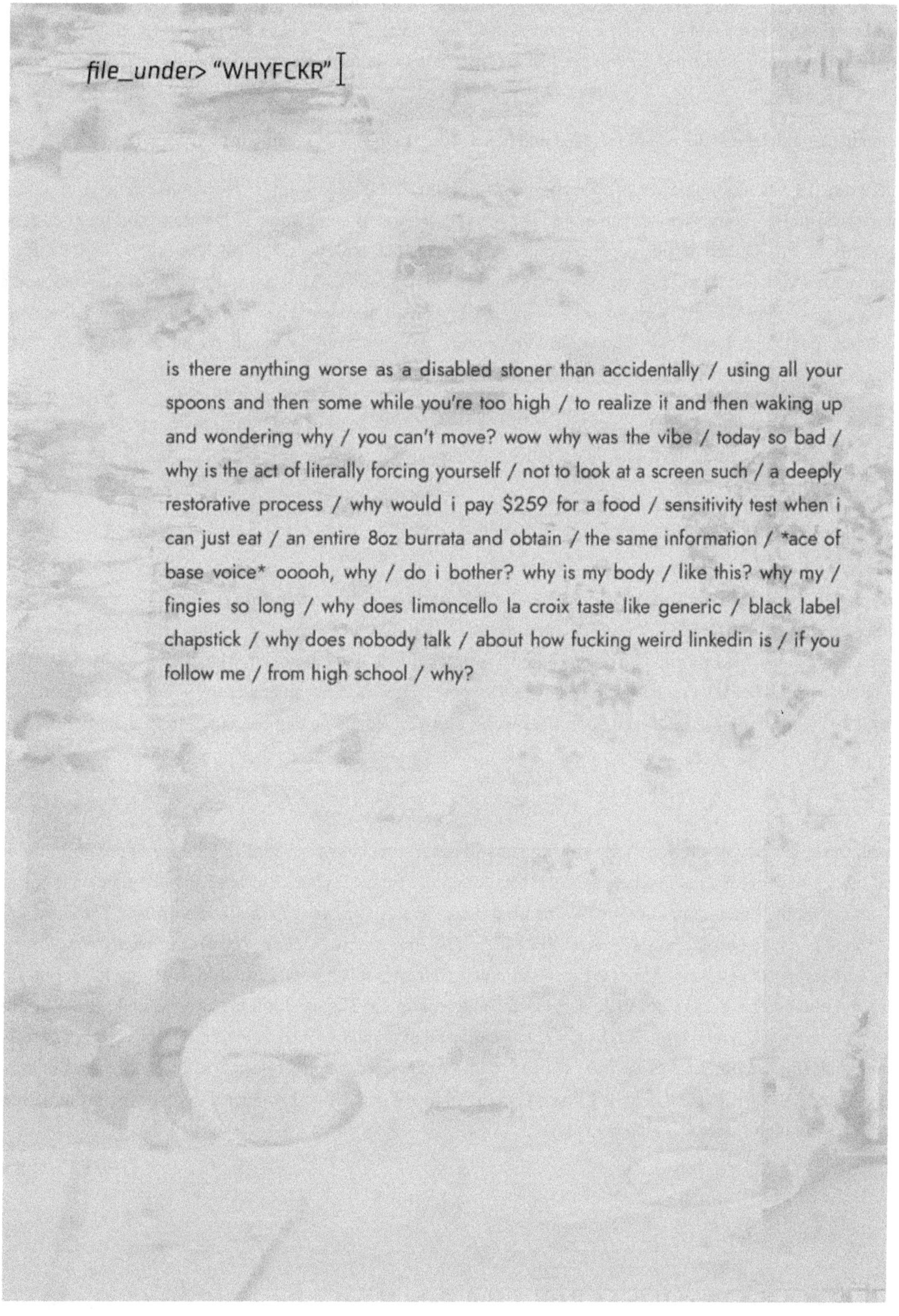
file_under> "WHYFCKR"
is there anything worse as a disabled stoner than accidentally / using all your spoons and then some while you're too high / to realize it and then waking up and wondering why / you can't move? wow why was the vibe / today so bad / why is the act of literally forcing yourself / not to look at a screen such / a deeply restorative process / why would i pay $259 for a food / sensitivity test when i can just eat / an entire 8oz burrata and obtain / the same information / *ace of base voice* ooooh, why / do i bother? why is my body / like this? why my / fingies so long / why does limoncello la croix taste like generic / black label chapstick / why does nobody talk / about how fucking weird linkedin is / if you follow me / from high school / why?

—nat raum—

This is how I write.

—Ali Smith

It's been over a year since I left teaching in public education in Orlando, Florida. Measuring the length of my mental breakdown is tricky because I reside in a state where "critical race theory" and "woke" are revised Republican bigoted buzzwords. But my mental illness and unemployed status "gift" me the luxury of getting lost in my daydreams. And my writing.

I study a small, bright image of Joan Didion's face and her words: "I am simply writing myself back to life."

Most of the time, it's late morning when my days begin–just before The Today Show's "Hoda and Jenna." I'm in bed with too many pillows, and my body is twisted up in the rose gold velvet duvet. Somewhere in the sea of soft textured fabric is my matching MacBook Pro. On the outside cover are stickers: "Mental Health Matters," "Pro-Choice, Pro-Feminist, Pro-Cat" and "Me and karma vibe like that." I sit up, swallow a daily rainbow of pills with last night's bottle of Smart Water, and pull the white Bahama shutters ¾ the way up, so my two cats can spy on all the darting lizards that scurry on the already hot and cracked concrete pool deck. Until yesterday, I didn't know that a group of lizards was called a "lounge." The slats of light and moving water are where my gaze lands. Everything's illuminated.

My wife, Sony, is gone by 6:50 am. Right before she leaves for her 10-hour shift at a veterinary clinic, she kisses me goodbye, whispers "Have a good day," and then a louder "I love you."

Then, I turn to my own words.

Avoidance.

I binge-watch Seasons 1 and 2 of *Succession* and revisit *Girls, black-ish*, and *Better Things*. I watch nearly every documentary on cults. I not so patiently wait for *The Last of Us*. Hulu, Apple +, Netflix, Prime, HBO Max, Peacock, Discovery +, and Disney + become close friends. Family at times. I hide from in-person friends and family. I say I'm "sick" when my body journeys between malaise and/or mania. I'm obsessed with the aesthetic of my soon-to-be website. Tacky "Sunshine State" vibes or ombré heathered hues. I'm awake, and I breathe in golden brilliance and exhale fuck it. I'm magic now.

Reading.

I stack up all the books by the left side of my too-big but still doesn't feel too-big bed. I'm giddy with possibilities. Horizontal titled spines are not in alphabetical order. I'm horizontal for large chunks of time and marinate on if "order" is the answer to all questions. I'm hungry to devour words from books like *Acceptance, In the Dream House, The Book of Delights, The Soul of the Octopus, Call Us What We Carry, The Best Essays of 2021, The Social Animal, Maybe You Should Talk to Someone*, and *Keep Moving*. I'm ecstatic that *Cultish* is this month's Audible selection. Instagram floods my feed with pop-cultured chronicles from Buzzfeed, Bustle, and Apartment Theory. I roll my eyes when I see "Why are Job Interviews a Neverending Nightmare?" on Vox. I hold steadfast that my daily ritual of reading from *Yoga Journal, The New York Times*, and *The Atlantic* teaches me things I need to know. The extensive screenshots of literary journal submission deadlines use up 3 MB of iCloud storage. It's time to put down my phone. Now. I wonder if my nightly insomnia searches protect me from my nightmares and hide my magic.

—Ali Smith—

Therapy.

I feel time driving north in the fog. Maybe I shouldn't be driving? I'm unsure of the definitions of "self-care" and "self-love" because they're co-opted by too many memes. And the term "self-help" is cringy because I can't manifest healing with only "help." Sometimes I like cringe. My therapist knows me far too well, so there's no room for banter, and bullshitting is banned just like some of the books in my public-school libraries. Again, *because Florida.* Suddenly my brain feels like it's on Space Mountain because I can't let the fascism in Florida go. My therapist rescues me from my rollercoaster of thoughts and reminds me about the end of last week's session. Is it true? Am I trying to write myself back to life? I was supposed to jot down a list of questions, but decades of sublingual benzodiazepines sometimes make my memory fuzzy. I wonder if I'm fucked because if I don't understand what to question, then, what about the answers? I sit on the office loveseat wrapped in a navy-weighted blanket. I hug a 20 x 20 pillow that reads "therapy is cool." It is. I ask my therapist to turn up the air. The temperature must be just right so I can breathe my boxed breathing. *Inhale one, two, three, four. Hold one, two, three, four. Exhale one, two, three, four. Repeat.* After 55 minutes I'm unsure what I just unpacked. But my anxiety has lessened, and the linear drive home feels safe. I can feel pending readiness.

Water.

I swim. I revel in fluidity. Ocean, swimming pool, river, stream, rain, and even a touristy water park. I love them all. I float on a raft, in a boat, and in a body. I type in *"how much water is in the human body?"* According to Google, *"For the first few months of life, nearly* three-fourths *of your body weight is made up of water. That percentage starts to decline before you reach your first birthday."* I believe this, even though it's the first answer to my question. I stop feeling sick because at least I learned how much my body holds. I come up for air. My body keeps score.

I languish in the surrounding sounds of waves and wet words.

—Ali Smith—

Praise

—*Christina D. Rodriguez*

—*Christina D. Rodriguez*—

Sit On Your Hands

—Mar Ovsheid

I'm keeping little pieces of graphite underneath my fingernails until they turn to diamonds. Then, I'll get them mined, polished, and set into rings. I'll ask you to be my life partner. I've got a jeweler picked out and everything.

"It's a crazy idea." The jeweler says.

I know it is.

"I'll do it."

I pay her in advance to show I'm serious.

You can't understand why I won't hold hands anymore. The secret reason is the little stones crushing into my nail beds, making we wince and nearly vomit. We stop going for walks together and I keep my hands in my pockets when you get too close.

"What are you drinking?"

Beers, mostly. Gin, often.

"Helps the pain."

"Pain?"

Oops.

"My head hurts. Been hurting."

"Ok."

You roll your eyes and sleep on the couch.

"I don't like how you sweat and smell after you drink."

I'm just a few more weeks from completing the compression when we go to a wedding and watch the newlyweds dance together. You've still got a little light left in your eyes for me.

You hold out a palm to coax me onto the floor.

"Come on, show me what you've got."

I shake my head. I can't. But I'm so inspired by the happy couple that I sit on my hands to try and speed up the process. You dance with one of the groomsmen and fall asleep on the car ride home.

The shortcut works, and two days later the diamonds are ready for extraction.

The jeweler removes the stones and ties gauze around my fingertips. She cleans the diamonds and sets them onto golden bands. I buy an expensive velvet box and place your ring inside.

I arrive home, bloody bandages still on my fingers, to find you putting your suitcases in the car. I stop you in your tracks, get down on one knee, and open the box. You glance at the rocks before turning away.

"You know I don't like diamonds." You toss your last bag of belongings into the trunk and slam it shut. "Besides, the way they source them is inhumane."

I permanently lose feeling in my fingertips, the only sensation a dull pain that occasionally radiates up my wrists and arms and to my heart. I sell the rings at a pawn shop for a numb fistful of cash and try to forget we ever held hands.

—Mar Ovsheid—

The Driver

—*Kevin Sampsell*

I saw a car driving down my street with its muffler on fire. I was sitting at the front window of my living room, eating breakfast and looking out, when it passed by. I wondered if the driver knew there was a fire behind him. I stepped out onto my porch to watch it slow at a Stop sign and turn the corner. I wondered if there would be an explosion.

The car was a silver Corolla. I had a therapist who once told me they drove a silver Corolla and it was the most common car in our city. I started seeing silver Corollas everywhere after that. He was right, as always. I started to imagine that everyone driving a silver Corolla was my therapist, even when it wasn't. I could hop in any silver Corolla and talk about my issues, my problems, my mother, my worsening diet.

Sometimes I make sunny side up eggs and carefully eat around the perfect yoke, saving it to the end. And then I tilt the plate to my open mouth and try to slide the unbroken yellow circle onto my tongue. Sometimes the circle is orange. I have successfully done this forty-nine times now.

I could see smoke in the sky, coming from the car. And then it was back on my street, as if it was just casually looping the neighborhood. I waved to the driver and mouthed the word *fire* at him and he did an angry gesture with his hand.

Minutes later, he was back, driving slower this time. His whole back bumper was in flames now. It reminded me of the gas burner on my stove, flickering fire.

I went back inside to call the police or the fire department. Both numbers were disconnected. Soon, there was a crowd of neighbors outside, with their phones out, waiting to record the car's return. But when the car once again turned onto our street, the neighbors pointed their phones at *me*. I didn't know what to do, so I tried to hide my face. The man in the car drove by, his window down now, and I could see through my fingers that he was sweating from the heat. His vehicle was half car, half fireball.

"Shoot him!" I called out to the neighbors, meaning with their cameras. But they kept their aim on me. I could smell the smoke in the air, so I went back inside to get away from all the commotion. I closed the door behind me and looked out the window. The neighbors were now filming something in a tree. It was a family of raccoons.

I tried to call the fire department again, but my phone died, so I took my breakfast plate and threw the unbroken egg yolk in the garbage. I filled the sink and washed my dishes, noticing that the air smelled clean again.

Later, as I prepared to make lunch (a turkey sandwich with cheese and a large pretzel), I heard another noise from the street. When I looked out, I saw the driver of the car running down the street, laughing loudly. His Corolla was nowhere to be seen, but now he was on fire. I wanted to help him but decided to pretend that it wasn't happening. I pinched myself but couldn't help looking again. At the Stop sign the man turned, his laughter and smoke trailing.

—*Kevin Sampsell*—

Daddys
—*Kevin Sampsell*

—*Kevin Sampsell*—

Without Give

—Crystal Sansom

Warm air swelled around me, muffled car horns and screeching brakes grated in the not too far distance. When I tried to pull my eyelids open, they were sealed. Uncurling from a fetal position, my limbs could not reach out. They strained against thick plastic. Something kept me in place. My arms could bend, and I ripped at my eyes, pulling duct tape from my skin and eyebrows. I did not make a sound. My breaths were short; I felt a bump and heard the gyrating wheels underneath me. I strained at the membrane that encapsulated me, thick and without give. I controlled my breathing, slow and calm. I'd been here before. The ride still took too long and I gave out.

When I woke, I lay on asphalt in front of a tall cityscape, people bustling around me. I wasn't even there. I stood, squinting into the sun. The building in front of me had three gargoyles that sat on the roof. Small spires separated them. They peered at me and I swallowed their glares.

I wandered for hours and came upon a park, trees bundled together in the middle. A few benches where those without homes tried to get a nap in. The park was more of a small forest and I entered. Greenery swiped at my bare arms; the air was cold within the tree cover. An ant mound was teeming with life. I sat on top of it. I closed my eyes to feel the ants climb over my body – red ants piercing me all over – and a presence was near me. The man leaned over me, the whites of his eyes a deep crimson. His breath smells of cotton candy as he touches his greasy nose to mine.

"We all have it in here."

He is now gone.

I do not know how to return home but I try.

Catalog of Go Home, You're Drunk
—*Megan Alyse*

Last night I didn't brush my teeth before bed

It was a humid way to rebel

Next time I see a crowded event, I'll stop by

My cat is my best friend

A sense of belonging is a hierarchical need

You got your food before you got your wine

Story of my life. Sorry about that

My therapist always admits to me how tired she is

People love the word *infused*

It's amazing how much a signature can do

I wonder what all my ex-husbands are drinking, eating

Getting married isn't all that hard, yet we congratulate

I'll answer to Babe after the third drink, third date

When recalling my first sexual experience, I cry

I glow in the heat

It's impossible to keep a mirror clean for very long

August: a crotch on the bus before the end of the line

I was working the room, rife with energy, thick with distraction

Charge a copay to credit

Credit a green tea shot to charge

It takes a village to support a watering hole

—*Megan Alyse*—

It takes a watering hole to support a village

No more bartenders, no more handsome men

No more sugar. No more clouds. No more summer rain

What I'm trying to say is nothing survives this heat

Twenty minutes from the beach but who has the time

The charcuterie needs more jam

Membership is a kind of home

What I'm trying to say is life is boring when it's good

To know the owner is everything

Stamp the card

Everyone wants rewards

Nothing seems dry

—Megan Alyse—

Situationship

—Megan Alyse

Autumn's end means it's been a year

A sigh in the distance means hard work is happening

They'll never finish paving that road

Sometimes I think I'm being watched

I walk down the street and pull at my skirt

It can be humid and chilly at the same time

I wonder just how flammable Spanish Moss can be

Demanded a porch swing in the agreement

He waits for me at the back door with a look

I tell my ex-husband I'm kind of happy

I see my lover once a week

There are fifty-two weeks in a year

There are few things we have in common

Not enough is subjective

Intimacy has something to do with eye contact

The wood grain shines under bee's wax

I lay out in the sun and feel a season

I season myself with shaving cream and lipstick

We are all different shades of something damaged

I learn about attachment theory and trauma bonds

In and out of connection is a tapping motion

—Megan Alyse—

Google photos has sent me a notification

Back and forth on the swing I rock

When can one count an anniversary

When can one admit to remembering

When does one apply all that they've learned

I don't know his friends' names

He's never been out with me on a Friday night

On and off is a kind of connection

Where the light goes so do my clothes

—Megan Alyse—

i am so dumb thinking about this makes me cry i am so dumb—tommy pico

—*Yael Villafranca*

—*Yael Villafranca*—

Cool, Famous, Good

—*Katy Haas*

I cut my bangs over the sink and wonder if you're thinking of me. Or if you're wondering whatever happened to all the gifts, the ones you gave me for my birthday and Christmas. Or your phone that I smashed on the pavement outside the music venue where your band played and only my friends showed up to watch. Or the boots I just bought with your credit card still saved to my Amazon account.

If you are, in fact, thinking of me, that's fine because I keep finding myself thinking of you. Even though you don't really see me when you look at me. But so what.

I cut my bangs and maybe you're thinking of what I looked like the last time you looked at me and really saw me, my old hair, my old shoes, my old jacket with the patches all over it, and you're thinking about the last time we had sex and how at the time you didn't realize it was going to be the last time we had sex, and you're thinking of the last time I said I loved you and how you didn't realize it was going to be the last time I said it.

Some mornings I wake up and I just want to tell you something that's always on the tip of my tongue but I can never figure out what it is. I check the manuals to all my kitchen appliances and they don't know either. To be honest with you: I hope you feel it when I throw away your favorite hoodie. I hope you feel it and know exactly how I feel and then you'll feel the way I feel: upside down.

I feel like a child when I wait for you to call from an unknown number from your new phone which I haven't yet smashed on the pavement in front of any music venue even though I want to.

When my phone does ring, it's only a telemarketer but I pretend it's a call from some very famous person just in case you're thinking of me and wondering if I've started talking to someone new. I pretend it's Dolly Parton and I'm Jolene. I pretend it's Armie Hammer and I say, "Armie, eat your heart out!" I pretend it's Lady Gaga and I tell her: "Everyday I am a meat dress." They always hang up first which I hope doesn't come back to you. I still want you to think I'm cool because I am cool, probably cooler than you even remember. I still want you to think I'm a good person, even though it's debatable whether or not I'm a good person and you never thought I was in the first place.

But the way I cut my bangs is very cool, and the boots I just bought are too. The way I talk to telemarketers like they're very famous people makes me seem like a good person. It must feel good to be mistaken for someone very famous, which never happens to me. Whenever we go around the table and say which celebrity each of us looks like, people look at me and say, "I don't know. You just look like you." It's so embarrassing to look like yourself and no one else but I pretend I'm cool with it, the way cool people do.

—*Katy Haas*—

Listen, I do want to be cool. I do not want to be anything like you. People still seem to like you in your old shoes with your old hair, but not enough to come see your band play at the music venue where I smashed your phone on the sidewalk. Tough break.

I stare in the mirror and I notice my bangs are crooked. The first thing I notice when I look at people is whether or not they have kind eyes. I don't even notice if their bangs are crooked or what their shoes look like.

When I first looked at you, you were wearing sunglasses but I still got the sense that your eyes were kind. And the reason I got that feeling is because of the fact that you didn't look at me. You looked away from me to a three-legged dog being walked down the side of the road. It's a small thing, but you made me feel ways that I maybe shouldn't have. So the times when you weren't looking at me and not really seeing me, you were looking away to whatever was moving nearby. I'm pretty sure one day I'll be able to figure out what exactly you were looking for in those moments but right now I can only think of dogs with three legs and birds flying into windows and women in short skirts with two nice legs. I don't wear short skirts and I feel insecure about my legs. Which isn't very cool, I know.

I ask Oprah Winfrey how she feels about her legs the next time she calls to ask me if I want to extend my warranty for the car that I don't own and she immediately hangs up on me. Can you believe it? I bet she doesn't ever cut her own hair. I bet she never wonders if someone is thinking about her. She just knows that they are. She never wonders if she's a good person. She just knows that she is.

—Katy Haas—

Biographies

Megan Alyse (She/Her), holds an MFA from Warren Wilson College. You can find some of her work appearing in *Angel City Review, Atticus Review, The Atlanta Review, Juked, Rattle,* and *The Rumpus.* Megan lives and writes in Savannah, GA. Connect with her on Instagram @megsalyse or at meganalyse.com.

Andi Benet [they|them] is a lens-based artist based out of San Francisco. Disabled and queer, their art is focused on questions of perception and identity, featuring dreamlike, distorted imagery and their own body in performative self-portraiture.

Jillian Calahan (she/they) is a poet and short story writer from Seattle, Washington. When she's not writing you can find her in a bookstore, chilling with her 4 cats and 2 dogs, crafting, or taking too many pictures of pretty sunsets. You can find her work on Instagram @novamarie_poetry

Alexis Dinkins grew up in New Haven, Connecticut. She received her MFA in Fiction from New England College, and her work can be read in *Pigeon Review, Stone Quarterly,* and *Salt Hill Journal.* She lives in Massachusetts with her pet tortoise, Salubrious!

Kate Garklavs (she/they) is a queer writer and artist living in Portland, OR. Her writing has appeared in *Juked, Wigleaf, Tammy,* and *Jubilat,* among other places, and their visual work has been showcased at the 2021 and 2022 PNWCC Paper Cuts exhibits and the 2022 Beaverton Arts Mixer, as well as in SoftQtrly and This House of Mine. Find her on Instagram at @therealgarky.

andrea lianne grabowski (she/her) is a midwestern lesbian writer occupying anishinaabe land. her published work lives in *HELL IS REAL* Anthology, *fifth wheel press, superfroot mag,* and elsewhere. you can find her making zines, on long drives being inspired by music, or peering in the windows of abandoned buildings.

Kelly Gray's writing recently appears or is forthcoming in *Witness Magazine, Southern Humanities Review, Permafrost, Trampset, Bear Review, Lunch Ticket,* and *Maudlin House.* She is the recipient of the Neutrino Short-Short Prize from *Passages North* and the ArtSurround Cohort Grant which funded her work with Pepperwood Preserve. Gray's collections include Instructions for an Animal Body (Moon Tide Press), and Tiger Paw, Tiger Paw, Knife, Knife (Quarter Press), MUD~ Field Notes from a Juvenile Psychiatric Institution (Bottlecap Press), and Quag Daughter (forthcoming from Dancing Girl Press). She's thrilled to have been recently selected to teach with California Poets in the Schools, and is hard at work creating a curriculum based on monsters, edges and lore. She lives with her family on unceded Coast Miwok Land in a very small cabin nine miles and seven fence posts away from the ocean.

Katy Haas is a queer non-binary poet, collage artist, and Furby enthusiast from mid-Michigan. Their work can be found in *Peach Magazine, HAD, Stanchion*, and elsewhere. Their chapbook *the algorithm knows i never stopped loving you* will be published by Bullshit Lit this year. Find them on Twitter (@katyydidnt) & Insta (@mouthshroom).

Tim Horvath (www.timhorvath.com) is the author of *Understories* (Bellevue Literary Press) and *Circulation* (sunnyoutside), as well as stories published or forthcoming in *Conjunctions, Passages North, Best Small Fictions 2021*, and elsewhere. He teaches in the MFA program for Creative Writing and Literature at Stony Brook, as well as at Phillips Exeter Academy and Manchester Community College. He is at work on a novel and a second collection.

Annaliese Jakimides is a writer and mixed media artist who grew up in inner-city Boston and raised a family on 40+ acres in northern Maine, growing almost all their food and pumping water by hand. Her poetry and prose have been broadcast on local and national public radio, and published in many magazines, journals (e.g., *Beloit Poetry Journal, Solstice*), and anthologies (most recently, *Breaking Bread, A Dangerous New World*). Nominated for the Pushcart Prize, she has been the recipient of the Acadia Prize for Poetry and a finalist for the Stephen Dunn Poetry Prize and the Maine Literary Awards, in both poetry and nonfiction, among others.

Aidan Jung is a multimedia artist whose creative identity developed at an early age while walking the city streets of Portland Oregon and Oakland California. As a young person navigating family and housing instability, Aidan practiced walking meditation as a methodology for grounding in self-attunement and spatial awareness. Currently, Aidan is using experimental techniques in Super 8 Film and Polaroid emulsion lifts to explore the city's animation of gender identity, queerness, urban decay and social solitude. Aidan studied film production and photography at the California College of Arts before finishing his degree and graduating from the Pacific Northwest College of Art with a BFA in 2017. With a decade of experience in film production, Aidan is a director and visual effects artist producing short films, music videos, and commercial content with the creative studio Ntropic in San Francisco, CA. Aidan is currently working on his first analogue photography book titled "Growing Pains". The project is a personal history of street photography illustrating the complexity of self-discovery and growth in the midst of social phobia and cultural division in the United States.

Carella is a three-time offender with Querencia Press, published in *Not Ghosts But Spirits*, the quarterly anthology, and now *Scavengers*. Her art and writing have appeared in numerous publications, including the cover of *Glassworks 26, Columbia Journal, Stripes Literary Magazine, Door is a Jar, Grub Street, Troublemaker Firestarter,* and *Sunday Mornings at the River.*

Catherine Kyle (she/her) is the author of *Fulgurite* (Cornerstone Press, forthcoming), *Shelter in Place* (Spuyten Duyvil, 2019), and other collections. She was the winner of the 2019-2020 COG Poetry Award and a finalist for the 2021 Mississippi Review Prize in poetry. She is an assistant professor at DigiPen Institute of Technology, where she teaches creative writing and literature.

Kyra Lambert (she/her) is a queer multidisciplinary artist whose works circulate around ideas of femininity, divinity and worship and take the form of jewelry, poetry and oil paintings. Lambert designs under the name 'Sacred Grotto'. With strong roots in Pagan practice, Kyra's work is emblematic of times past and the ocean's offerings. Lambert is currently based in Halifax, NS and has received an emerging artist designation from the Canadian Council for the Arts.

Donica Larade (she/they) is a multidisciplinary artist currently based out of Kjipuktuk Nova Scotia exploring a variety of concepts using watercolour, print and mixed media. Primarily creating scientific illustrations of local wildlife, they also explore body positivity, chronic pain, queer art, or pop culture autobiographical cartoons, they create unique pieces through the lens of their background in science.

Rebecca Lauer, a 2022 graduate from the University of California Riverside Low Residency MFA. She lives in Portland Oregon writing scary stories about monsters and supernatural creatures.

Francesca Leader is a self-taught writer and artist originally from Western Montana. Her writing has appeared or is forthcoming in *Wigleaf, Fictive Dream, Barren, CutBank, the Leon Literary Review, JMWW, the Mom Egg Review, Roi Fainéant, the Harpy Hybrid Review*, and elsewhere. Learn more about her work at inabucketthebook.wordpress.com.

Hillary Leftwich is the author of two books. She teaches creative writing to challenged and incarcerated youth for two local nonprofits. She focuses her writing on class struggle, single motherhood, trauma, mental illness, the supernatural, ritual, and the impact of neurological disease. She is an advocate for her son and others who live with epilepsy, and other survivors of DV. She teaches Tarot and Tarot writing workshops focusing on strengthening divination abilities and writing. She was born and raised in Colorado Springs, CO, and currently lives in Denver.

Delilah Martinez has been previously published in *Gaze Journal* and the *Oregon City Digest*. She is also in the process of obtaining her MFA in Creative Non-Fiction at Portland State University. She is finding parts of herself in every rain cloud.

Maddie McGalliard is an amateur analog collage artist, painter, and poet. Her work explores connections between nature, queerness, and mental health. She lives in Portland, Oregon.

Jill Michelle's latest poems appear/are forthcoming in *Hole in the Head Review, Kissing Dynamite, Rise Up Review, SWWIM Every Day* and *Valley Voices*. She teaches at Valencia College in Orlando, Florida. Find more of her work at byjillmichelle.com.

Reverie Koniecki is a writer and educator living in Dallas, Texas. She earned her MFA in Poetry and Creative Nonfiction from New England College. Her work has appeared in *Guernica, Multiplicity, HeavyFeather Review, Post Road* and other places. Her two chapbooks, to the god of sore feet and The Wars That Steer Us are forthcoming in 2023.

—Biographies—

Darla Mottram (she/they) lives and writes in Portland, Oregon. She is a graduate of Portland State University's MFA in poetry, and is currently a freelance educational writer. Her poetry, fiction, and creative nonfiction have appeared in print and online, most recently at *Old Pal, Dream Pop Press*, and *Queen Mob's Teahouse*.

C.E. O'Banion is a writer and father of two living in Baton Rouge, LA. His work can be found in *The Southern Review, Mouthing Off Magazine, The Dead Mule*, and more. His debut novel, *Chinese New Year,* was released March of 2023. For more of his work, visit: www.ceobanion.com

Tiffany Overby lives in Portland, Oregon. She is inspired by elements of natural world and her continued practices of observation and gratitude.

Mar Ovsheid is a spoilsport who tragically dropped—and lost—her sea monkeys in the carpet as a kid. Her work has been featured in *Cream Scene Carnival, Los Suelos, Mulberry Literary,* and *oranges journal*, among others. Mar works as a housekeeper and is visible at @mar_ovsheid on Instagram.

Celeste Perez is a poet and writing instructor. She received an MFA in creative writing from Emerson College. She lives in Portland, Oregon.

nat raum (b. 1996) is a disabled artist, writer, and genderless disaster from Baltimore, MD. They're the editor-in-chief of fifth wheel press, as well as the author of *you stupid slut, the abyss is staring back, random access memory*, and several chapbooks. Find them online: natraum.com/links.

Christina D. Rodriguez (she/her/hers), a Latinx poet in Chicago, is the author of *Knees in the Garden* (Querencia Press, 2023). Her poems have appeared in various journals and anthologies. She is a board member of the Chicago Writers Association and poetry editor for the CWA's *The Write City Magazine*. Find Christina at crodonline.info or @poemlust on Instagram.

Kevin Sampsell is a collage artist, writer, publisher, and bookseller. His writing has appeared in publications like *Longreads, Salon, The Rumpus, Poetry Northwest, McSweeney's*, and elsewhere. His books include the memoir *A Common Pornography*, the novel *This Is Between Us*, and a book of collages and poems, *I Made an Accident*, published in summer of 2022. He lives in Portland, Oregon, and runs the small press Future Tense Books.

Ami J. Sanghvi (he/him, they/them) is an Indian-American author, artist, designer, and boxer with an M.F.A. in Creative Writing from the California Institute of the Arts. They are the Co-Founder of *Gutslut Press*, as well as the author of *Confessions of a Baby Vamp: Letters to John Milton* (*Gutslut Press* '21), *Lipstick[less] Mania: A Ritual For No One* (*Bottlecap Press* '22), *Into Oblivion* (*Sweat-Drenched Press* '22), *x( )-id </3* (*Trickhouse Press* '22), and *In Residuum* (*Kith*

Books '23), among others. Their work can be found in numerous places, including *Peach Magazine, So It Goes: The Literary Journal of the Kurt Vonnegut Museum and Library*, and *Inverted Syntax*, with more forthcoming in *Fence*. Link: linktr.ee/hotwraithbones Twitter/IG: @HotWraithBones

Crystal Sansom is a cemeterian and English educator living in Knoxville, TN. She is a lecturer at the University of Tennessee. Crystal holds a Bachelor of Arts in Visual Art, a Bachelor of Arts in English, as well as a Master's of English, all conferred from Western Carolina University in Cullowhee, NC. She also holds a Master's of Fine Arts degree in Fiction Writing from New England College in Henniker, NH. Her work has been featured in *The Spectre Review* and *50 Word Stories*.

Ali Smith (she/her) is a queer Gemini who collects invisible illnesses. She is a nonfiction writer, educator, and freelance editor. Her advocacy work focuses on mental health awareness and addressing equity issues in education. Currently, she is working on a creative nonfiction project surrounding memory, loss, the body as "home," healing, and growing up in Central Florida. She dreams of living in a fancy pink hotel. Follow her at @a.denee_light_bright.

Dia VanGuten & Beppi: "Heart of December" is from The Undeads- a Collection of Pink Zombie Rose Comics, written by Dia and illustrated by Beppi. Known only as "Beppi" in the comicpedia, no last name needed, the artist has worked in comics, textiles, sculpture and fine arts. She explores culture and experiments with form. Dia does the same in her work. The author was a decade into Pink Zombie Rose when she realized she was writing a series of graphic novels. She went straight to Beppi. To learn more about PZR https://www.instagram.com/pinkzombierose/www.pinkzombierose.com To learn more about Beppi, https://www.instagram.com/beppiisbertwww.circleofevil.com To learn more about Dia - www.diavangunten.com (Dia is EIC of Cream Scene Carnival, @creamscenecarnival. Beppi is a curator for the magazine.) "Heart of December" was originally published as a short story, by Fatal Flaw, so the text-only version can be read here https://www.fatalflawlit.com/fiction-pieces/heart-of-december

Yael Villafranca (she/they) is a queer immigrant Filipine American artist. She was born in Manila, Philippines, grew up in the Central Valley and Bay Area of California, and currently resides in Portland, OR. Find her on Instagram @yael_villafranca or at her 100% real and not-spam website, www.yaelv.xyz

—Biographies—

CPSIA information can be obtained
at www.ICGtesting.com
Printed in the USA
BVHW021143110423
662126BV00016B/747